level 1

TECHNIC
LESSONS

by JAMES BASTIEN

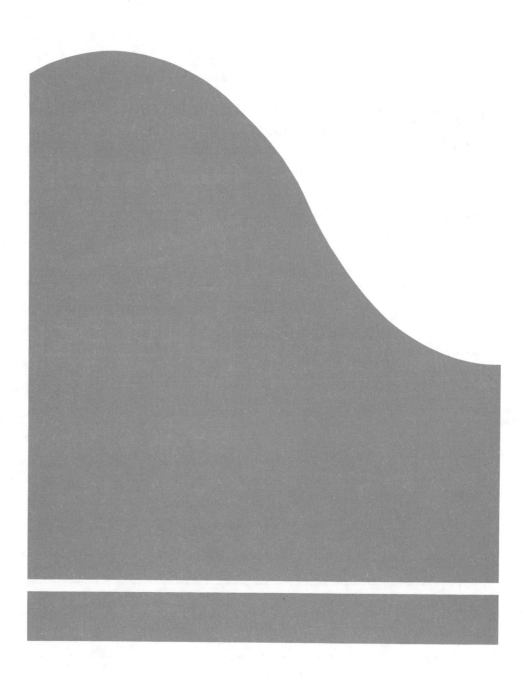

KJOS WEST · Neil A. Kjos, Jr. Publisher · San Diego, California

TO THE TEACHER

TECHNIC LESSONS, Level 1, is designed to be used simultaneously with **PIANO LESSONS, Level 1** (© *1976 KJOS WEST, San Diego, California. Ed. No. WP2).* It may also be used with any piano course.

DYNAMICS   Unless indicated, the dynamics are to be suggested by the teacher. On each repeat of the exercise, have the student use a different dynamic level.

TEMPO   Direct the student to play each exercise in three tempos: slow, medium and fast. On each repeat, have the student use a different tempo.

TOUCH   Unless staccato is indicated, the basic touch for these exercises is legato. However, many of the legato exercises may be repeated played staccato at the teacher's discretion.

The goal of **TECHNIC LESSONS** is to develop hand and finger coordination and facility, and to develop ease and control at the keyboard. A variety of keyboard experiences is provided to give the student a basic foundation in beginning fundamentals.

Suggested Use of Materials with "PIANO LESSONS, Level 1."

SHEET MUSIC from **Level One Solos** may be assigned to the student at the teacher's discretion.

ISBN 0-8497-5011-3

TO THE STUDENT

The studies in this book are designed to help you play the piano with ease and control. Allow time each day for technic practice. You might use these studies as warm-ups before beginning to practice your pieces.

Think of these three points often.

HEIGHT — Sit up high enough to reach the keys easily. Your wrists and forearms should be in a *straight line* over the keys. Do you have a piano stool or a piano chair at home which moves up and down? If not, cushions or telephone books will help raise you up when you practice.

POSTURE — Sit up *straight* in front of the center of the piano (by the piano's name). Place your feet flat on the floor. Do your feet reach the floor? If not, it is helpful to have a foot-stool under them when you practice.

HAND POSITION — When playing the piano, hold your fingers in a nice *curved shape*. Imagine you are holding a ball. This is the way the fingers should be curved when playing the piano.

CONTENTS

BEGINNING MUSIC FACTS

The following music facts are given for review and reference.

STAFFS - CLEFS

GRAND STAFF

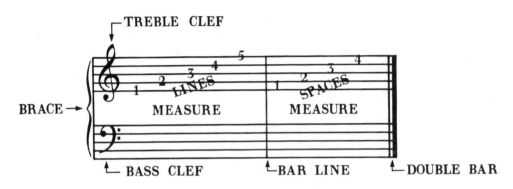

KEYBOARD - NOTES

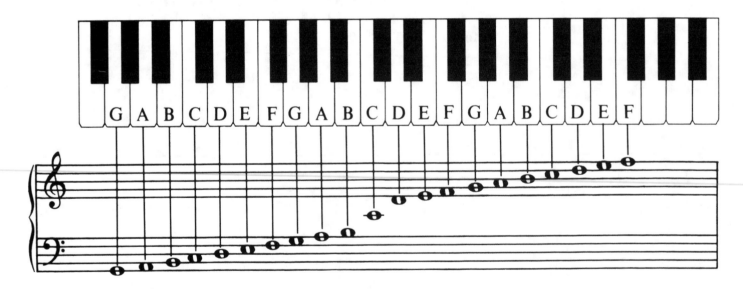

SHARPS - FLATS

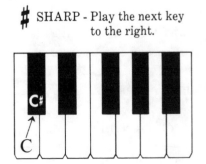

♯ SHARP - Play the next key to the right.

♭ FLAT - Play the next key to the left.

NOTE VALUES - RESTS

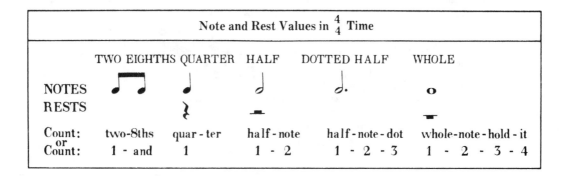

	TWO EIGHTHS	QUARTER	HALF	DOTTED HALF	WHOLE
NOTES	♫	♩	𝅗𝅥	𝅗𝅥.	𝅝
RESTS		𝄽	▬		▬
Count:	two-8ths	quar-ter	half-note	half-note-dot	whole-note-hold-it
or Count:	1 - and	1	1 - 2	1 - 2 - 3	1 - 2 - 3 - 4

INTERVALS

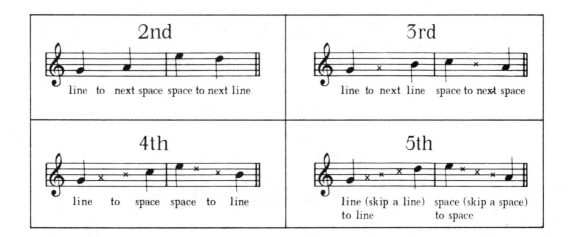

2nd — line to next space   space to next line

3rd — line to next line   space to next space

4th — line to space   space to line

5th — line (skip a line) to line   space (skip a space) to space

TIME SIGNATURES

2/4   2 beats in each measure. the quarter note (♩) gets one beat.

3/4   3 beats in each measure. the quarter note (♩) gets one beat.

4/4   4 beats in each measure. the quarter note (♩) gets one beat.

TERMS

Forte f means loud.

Legato   Play connected tones smoothly.

Piano p means soft.

Slur   A curved line over ⌢ or under ⌣ two or more notes that are to be played legato.

Staccato   Play disconnected tones in a short separated way. A dot above (♩̇) or below (♩.) a note means to play staccato.

Tie   A curved line which connects notes on the same line 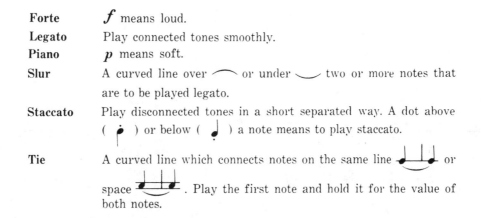 or space ⌣. Play the first note and hold it for the value of both notes.

C MAJOR FIVE FINGER PATTERNS

WARM~UPS

SLOW WORK~OUT

FAST WORK~OUT!

SKIPPING

SKIPPING, STEPPING

SKIPPING FAST!

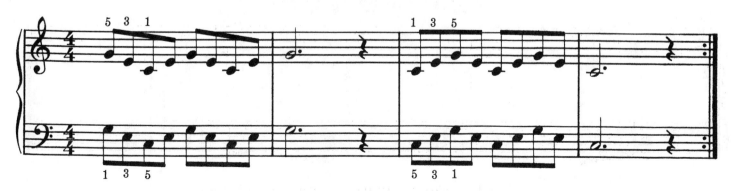

CHORDS

GOING UPHILL

broken chord *block chord*

ENGINE STARTING

GIANT STEPS!

l. h. over *l. h.*

TUMBLING

WARM-UPS

LITTLE SONG

*TEACHER: The three-note V7 chord is introduced in "PIANO LESSONS, Level 2."

STACCATO

WARM~UP HOPS

KANGAROO HOPS

FAST HOPS!

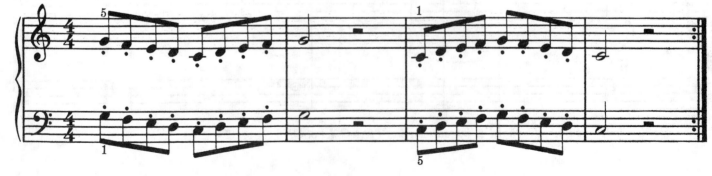

PHRASING

DROP~LIFT 1.

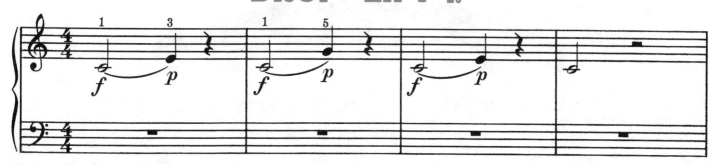

DROP~LIFT 2.

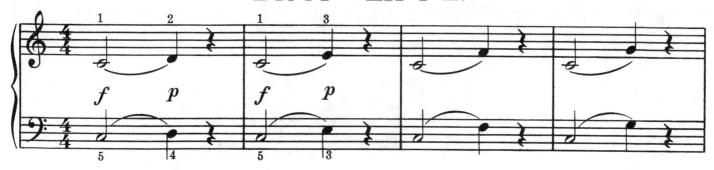

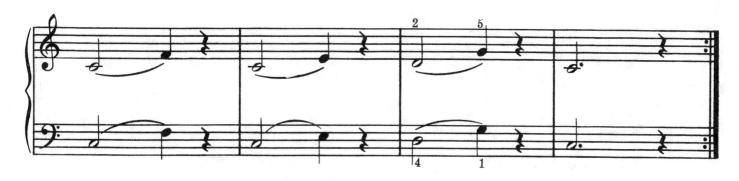

CONTRARY MOTION

THE ESCALATOR

Going up

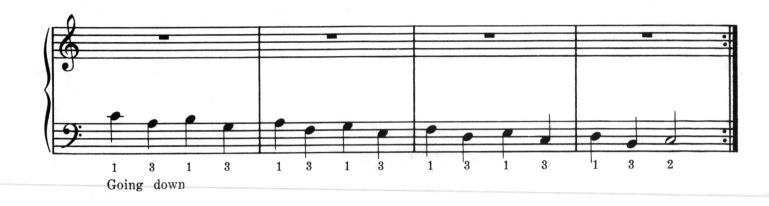

Going down

JAPANESE FAN

THUMB CROSSINGS

TURN ME UNDER

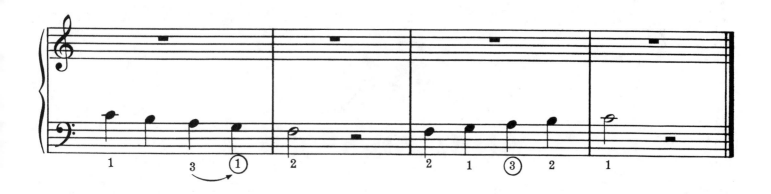

TURN ME UNDER, AGAIN

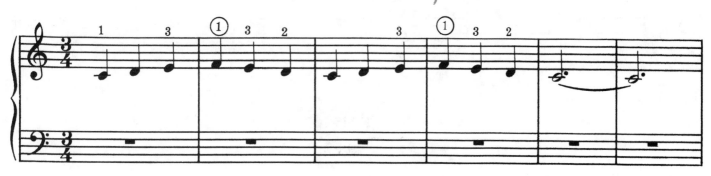

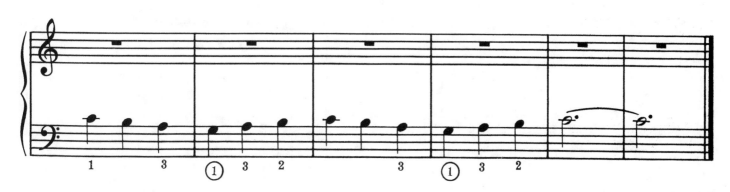

14

F MAJOR FIVE FINGER PATTERNS

WARM~UPS

SLOW WORK~OUT

FAST WORK~OUT!

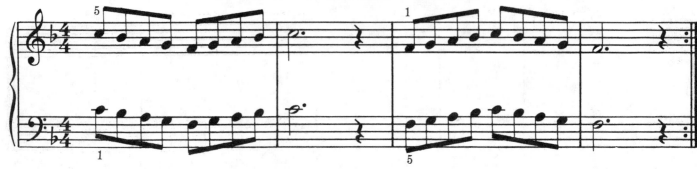

SKIPPING

SKIPPING, AGAIN

SKIPPING FAST!

CHORDS

CRAWLING

OFF WE GO!

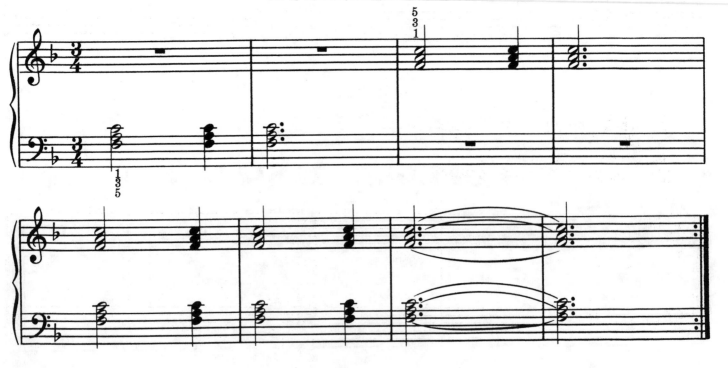

LOOP THE LOOP

WARM-UPS

MORNING SONG

STACCATO ~ LEGATO

HOP ~ SLIDE

HOP ~ STEP

PHRASING

SWINGING

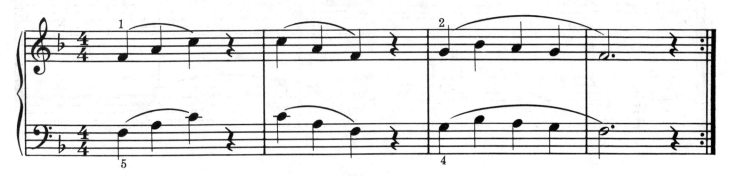

FLOATING RIGHT, FLOATING LEFT

G MAJOR FIVE FINGER PATTERNS

WALKING ~ RUNNING

TRICKY STEPS 1.

TRICKY STEPS 2.

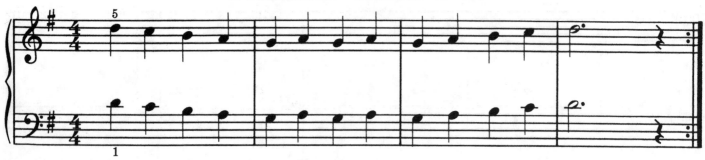

STRETCHING UP

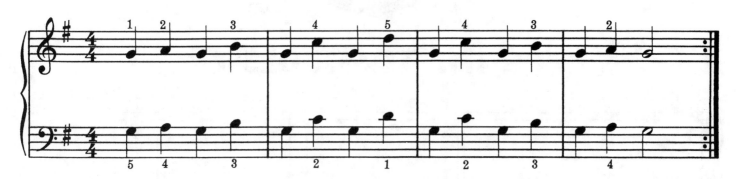

STRETCHING DOWN

SKIPPING FAST!

CHORDS

ON THE TRAMPOLINE

STEAMBOAT PUFFING

LOOP THE LOOP

WARM-UPS

EVENING SONG

STACCATO ~ LEGATO

HOP, GLIDE 1.

HOP, GLIDE 2.

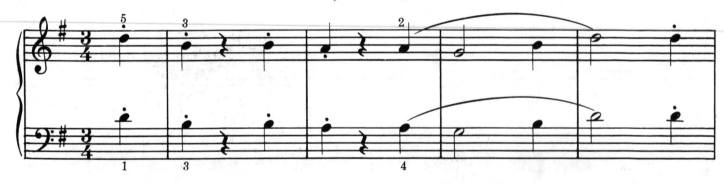

PHRASING ~ CONTRARY MOTION

DROP~LIFT

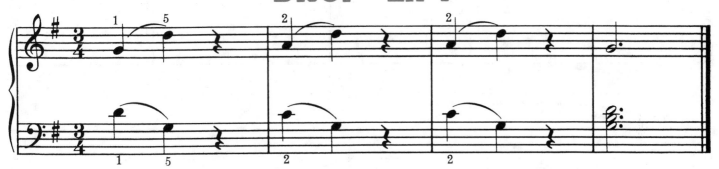

DROP~FLOAT OFF

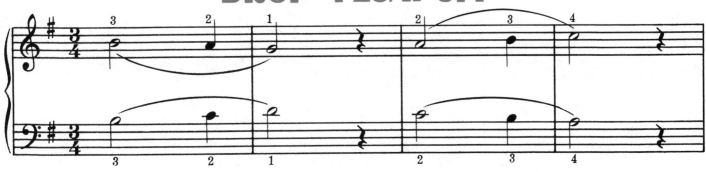

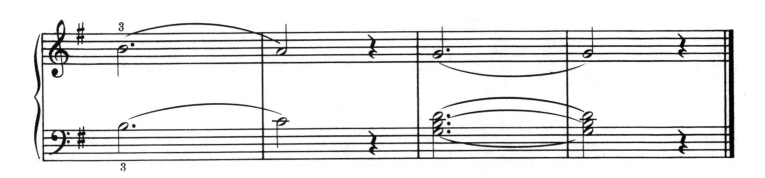

MOVING HAND POSITIONS

BUSY FINGERS!

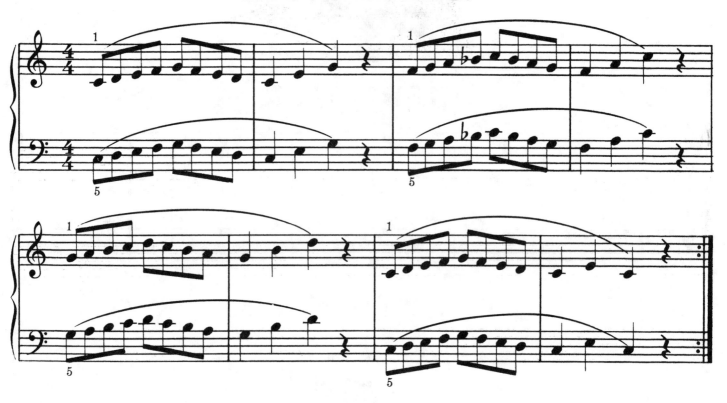

KEEP YOUR BALANCE

DOTTED RHYTHM

THE BALKY MULE!

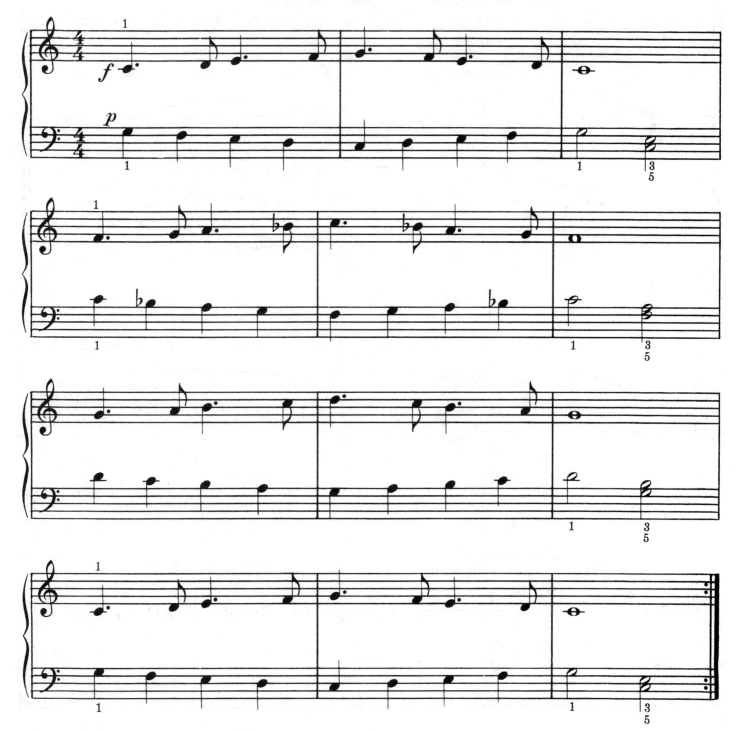

THUMB CROSSINGS

CATCH ME!

CHROMATICS

BEE BUZZING

MOSQUITO BUZZING

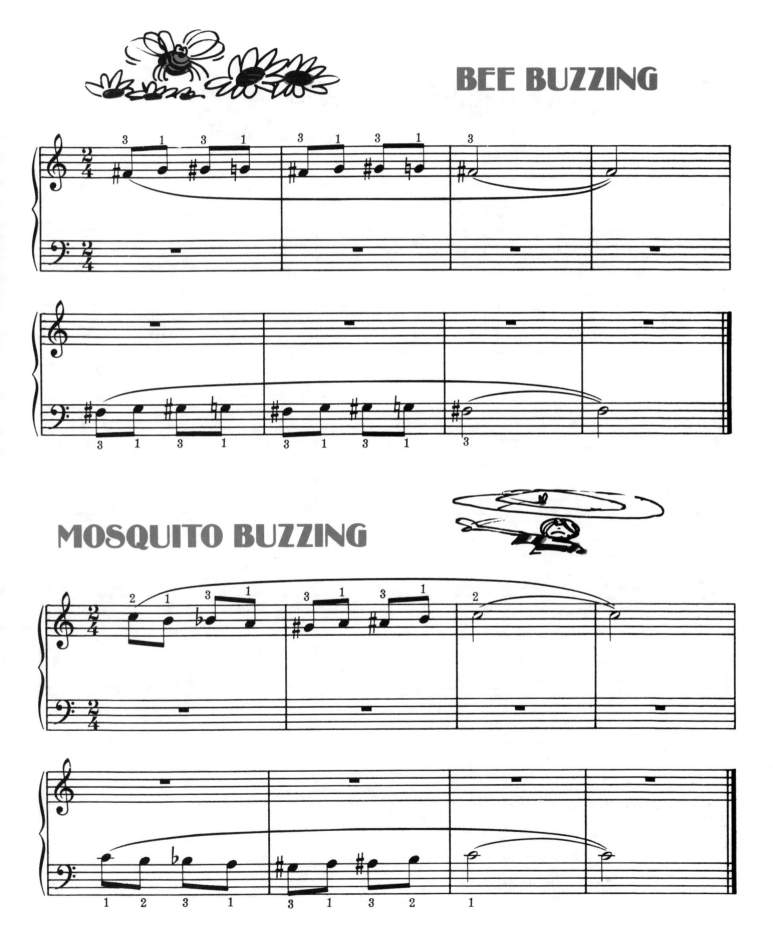

PEDAL

THE HARP SONG

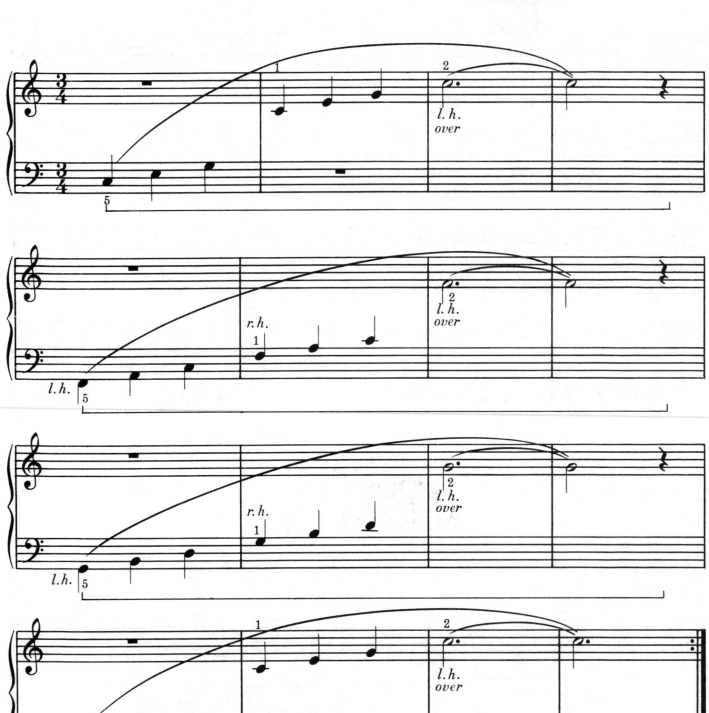

DOUBLE NOTES

TWO'S COMPANY

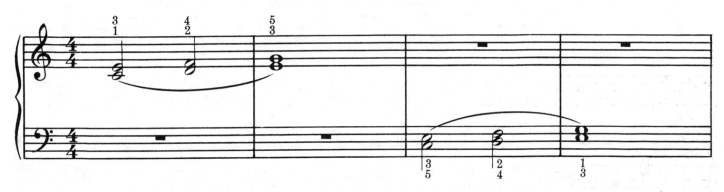

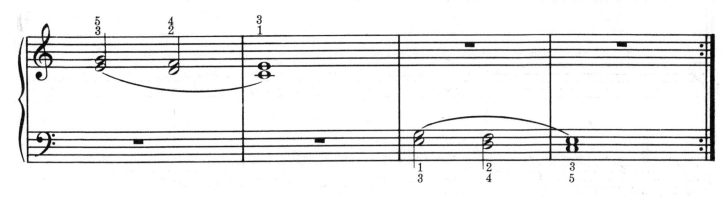

TOO MUCH FUN!

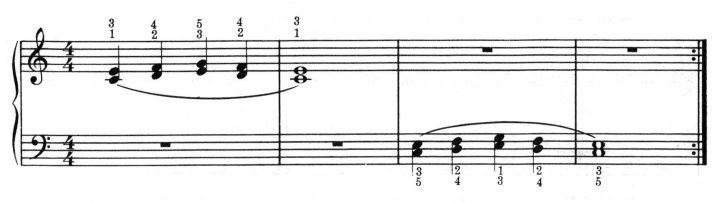

TEACHER'S TECHNIC